MAHABHARATA

PART 3

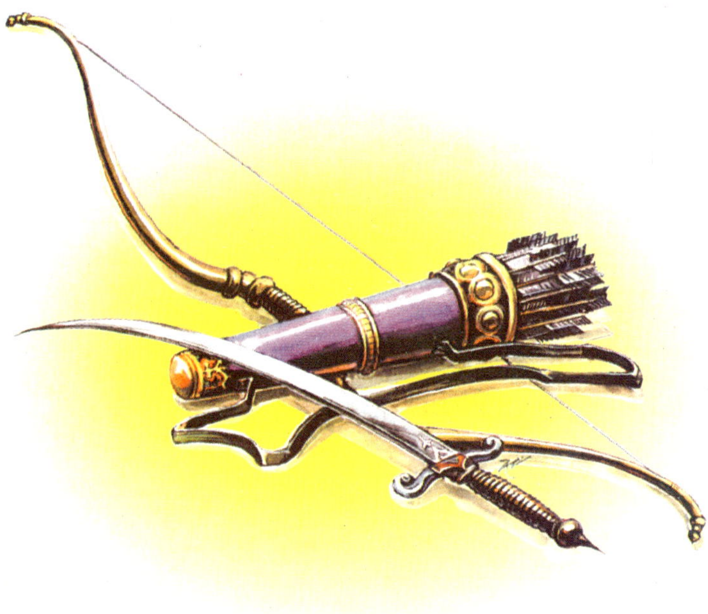

Artwork By:
K.L. Verma

Retold & Edited By:
T.R. Bhanot

DREAMLAND PUBLICATIONS

J-128, KIRTI NAGAR, NEW DELHI - 110 015 (INDIA)
Phone : 2545 5657, 2510 6050 Fax. : (011) 2543 8283
e-mail : dreamland@vsnl.com
www.dreamlandpublications.com

We have read in the foregoing book of this series that the Pandavas, having left the town of Ekchakra, came to the bank of the river Ganga where they had to confront and checkmate Angaarparna who gave two very useful presents to Arjuna—the first being *Chakshushee* (the power to see anything at any time and at any place in all the three worlds) and the second being one hundred heavenly horses of the 'Gandharvas'.

Leaving the horses in the custody of Angaarparna and to demand them when required, the Pandavas advanced on their way.

Roaming about here and there, the Pandavas came to know that Drupad, King of Panchal, was going to hold the *swayamvar* of his daughter. So, they set out

for Panchal along with their mother Kunti to take part in the royal event.

As the Pandavas were disguised as Brahmanas, a number of other Brahmanas joined them to reach Panchal. They knew that the Princes coming to participate in the swayamvar would give food and clothes in charity to them in order to win the goodwill of Drupad and his daughter.

The Brahmanas did not know at all about the identity of the Pandavas except sage Ayudhaumya who had agreed to act as the Priest of the Pandavas.

After a long and tiring journey of several days, the party reached Panchal. The Pandavas went about the Capital town that was beautifully decorated with Reception Gates at every step. They came to hear of the divine beauty of the princess, especially of her locks of hair. The day for the 'swayamvar' approached and the suitors assembled in the pandal.

The Pandavas also reached the venue at the appointed time and took their seats among the Brahmanas.

The gathering consisted of princes and kings of various kingdoms and sages known for their wisdom and learning. Every participant was being properly greeted and honoured by king Drupad. When everybody had taken his seat,

King Drupad stood up and announced that his daughter, Draupadi, was going to enter the venue. Bugles and drums started playing and strains of melodious music filled the atmosphere to mark the entry of the princess accompanied by her brother Dhrishtadyumna. Adorned exquisitely from top to toe, she looked no less than a heavenly nymph. At once, all eyes were turned to her.

As for the Pandavas, nobody could take notice of their presence except Krishna, ruler of Dwarika, who had come there with his brother Balrama. He told him about the escape of the Pandavas and their presence in the 'swayamvar' as well.

How could Arjuna remain a silent spectator to the grave situation ? Grabbing his bow and the quiver of arrows, he took position with a view to facing the onslaught of the haughty Princes.

The Brahmanas stood up with their *trishuls* aimed at the advancing Kings giving out a loud war-cry—*Jai Shankar*—and assuring Arjuna that they were with him.

Arjuna, waving his hand to check the Brahmanas from being agitated, said, "Rest assured ; I alone am more than a match for them all. You have got simply to wait and watch."

Saying so, Arjuna began shooting arrows at the advancing Princes and most of them fell senseless on the ground.

Arjuna's brothers, Krishna and Balrama were smiling to see what was happening. Arjuna was showering volleys of arrows ruthlessly at the Kings who either took to their heels or fell down unconscious. Duryodhana then sent someone to call Karna who had left the venue out of resentment.

When Karna came, Duryodhana instigated him saying, "Karna ! kill him ; it is not a sin to kill a Brahmana in a war." Karna got ready with his bow and arrows.

Setting arrows to his bow, Karna began to shoot at Arjuna. But Arjuna was so furious that his arrows soon sent Karna out of wits and he fell down senseless.

When he came to himself, he said, "O valiant young man ! I am very impressed with your skill at archery. It was only Arjuna who could face me."

"But you have not only done it but beaten me as well. You can be none else but Lord Indra or Lord Vishnu in disguise."

"I am neither of these ; I am a humble Brahmana and the credit of my skill goes to my great Guru who has taught me the use of heavenly weapons like *Indrastra* and *Brahmastra*," retorted Arjuna.

Hearing these words, Karna stopped fighting with high words of applause for his opponent.

Seeing the Princes taking up a wrong course, Bheema's blood had boiled and he, uprooting a thick post, had been ready to charge at the advancing Princes.

It was king Shalya who came first of all to face Bheema. Throwing his post aside, Bheema lifted Shalya above his head and flung him down with a thud.

Seeing the fall of Shalya and finding Karna hesitant of facing the valiant Brahmana, the panicked Princes thought it better to flee from the venue.

Arjuna, then, cleared the way from among the confused gathering and made for the place where his mother Kunti had been waiting for them. Evidently, his brothers and Draupadi followed him.

Soon they reached the place to find Kunti busy in prayers. Draupadi's brother, Prince Dhrishtadyumna, had secretly followed the Pandavas.

Entering Kunti's room, all the five brothers shouted in joy, "Look mother ! what have we brought today ?" Kunti had her back towards them as she was

sitting facing the idol of Shiva. Without turning her face to them, she said, "Divide it equally among yourselves all the five of you."

She never knew that her sons were talking of Draupadi whom Arjuna had won in the 'swayamvar'. She thought that they were talking of the alms which they usually brought after their daily round.

But soon, she took notice of Draupadi and felt highly embarrassed at what she had said. So, she said, "My sons ! I was under an impression that you had brought something special by way of alms from a charitable wealthy person. That was why I directed you to share it equally."

Kunti was really repentant of what she had said because her words could not be fulfilled without forcing Draupadi into a social sin. So, she felt highly worried and ashamed as well.

Draupadi, when she saw her mother-in-law in deep anguish, consoled her saying, "Mother ! don't worry at all ; I was blessed with a boon to have five husbands when sent to this earth from heaven. How can the boon conferred on me by gods be false ? It has come true and I have no whims about it."

Just at that moment, Lord Krishna and his brother Balrama reached there. They touched Kunti's feet out of respect and then greeted Yudhishthir. They had recognised the Pandavas at the venue of the swayamvar itself.

Hearing Krishna's words, all the Pandavas were highly astonished. Then, taking leave of them, Krishna made for Dwarika along with Balrama.

As for Draupadi, her joy knew no bounds when she came to know that it was valiant Arjuna who had won her fulfilling the condition of the swayamvar. She thanked her stars to become a bride of the royal family of Hastinapur and to be the spouse of the brave Pandavas.

As already mentioned, Dhrishtadyumna, Draupadi's brother, had stealthily followed the Pandavas and his sister. He had heard the conversation between Kunti and the Pandavas as well as that between Krishna and Yudhishthir. So, he had become fully aware of the reality. Bubbling with delight, he rushed to the palace to disclose the pleasant news to his father.

As soon as he came face to face with King Drupad, he was asked about the young man who had won Draupadi.

"There is nothing to worry at all, dear father. My sister has gone as a bride to the famous royal family of Hastinapur. The brave youth who is your son-in-law is none else but Arjuna, the famous archer," replied Dhrishtadyumna.

"Are you in your sense indeed ? All the Pandavas had been burnt alive by wicked Duryodhana in the lac-palace. How is it possible then that my daughter has been won as a bride by Arjuna ?" argued king Drupad.

"Nay, father! the Pandavas had escaped the death-trap through a tunnel from the lac-palace. They had been living in disguise since then. They came to our Capital to take part in the 'swayamvar'. They were staying at a potter's house in our city at that time," explained the Prince.

King Drupad, when he came to know the reality about the Pandavas, was beside himself with joy. At once, he ordered that stately arrangements should be made for according a royal reception to them and their dear mother Kunti.

The palace was bedecked with flowers, perfumes, bunting and other decorative articles. It was profusely illuminated at night too. Then, the Pandavas were invited so that the marriage of Draupadi could be performed according to the prescribed rites.

When the King was busy welcoming the Pandavas, Saint Vyasa happened to reach there. The King, touching the feet of the Saint, welcomed him too.

The King put forward a query before the Saint, "Sir, I am puzzled to think how it will be possible for my daughter to have five husbands without violating the religious as well as the social codes."

The Saint asked the King not to feel perturbed because it was to happen inevitably because of the boon, granted by Lord Shiva to Draupadi on the eve of sending her to the earth.

So, the King's doubts came to be set at rest and Draupadi's marriage was performed with all the five Pandavas.

News about the Pandavas was constantly reaching Vidur, the Prime Minister of Hastinapur, through his spies. But Duryodhana and Dhritrashtra believed that the Pandavas had been burnt alive along with their mother Kunti.

Now that the marriage of Draupadi with the Pandavas had exposed them, Vidur thought it desirable to inform Dhritrashtra of it.

Vidur went to Dhritrashtra and said, "Your Majesty ! the Pandavas are alive along with their mother. The young man, who fulfilled the condition of the swayamvar at Panchal, was none else but your nephew Arjuna. According to

the boon conferred on Draupadi by Lord Shiva, Drupad has married off her to all the five Pandavas through a royal ceremony."

Hearing this, Dhritrashtra put on a broad smile to express his joy, though it was only fake and apparent.

Dhritrashtra asked Vidur to prepare beautiful garments and valuable ornaments for Draupadi as well as for his nephews. The King further asked Vidur to ask Duryodhana to go to Panchal and escort the Pandavas back to Hastinapur along with Kunti and Draupadi. Vidur bowed low before the King and went away.

Just then, Duryodhana came there along with Karna. In fact, they had overheard what Vidur had told the King and also what the King had asked him to do. Duryodhana said to Dhritrashtra, "Dear Father ! I have heard everything. I will request you not to make the mistake of giving any lift to the Pandavas. It is sure to prove suicidal one day."

Karna forcefully seconded what Duryodhana had said.

"My Son ! don't take me to be a child. I realise the danger equally well. But you know that Vidur is a staunch supporter of the Pandavas. So, it was advisable on my part to say so. Should we disclose our real feelings to him ?"

"Let me know what your plans are. We must do something so that the Pandavas are not able to raise the question of demanding their father's kingdom back for themselves," argued Dhritrashtra.

Duryodhana said, "I wish that Bheema must be killed somehow or the other. He is the mightiest of all the Pandavas. With his death, half their strength will be gone and they would never take courage to raise their eyes towards the throne of Hastinapur. Another step worth taking is that we should instigate Drupad and his son against the Pandavas for forcing Draupadi to marry all of them through their mother Kunti."

Hearing Duryodhana's words, Karna reacted saying, "Duryodhana ! your plan in regard to Bheema is all right. But as far as Druapd is concerned, he is a man of very strong character. He would never go against the Pandavas even for your entire kingdom. Why don't you follow that he did not hesitate to give his daughter to them though they were paupers at that time ?"

"What should we do then, Karna ?" asked Duryodhana and his father together.

Karna replied, "The only choice left with us now is to make war on Panchal, defeat the forces of Drupad and capture Drupad, his son along with the Pandavas, their mother and Draupadi herself. This step is sure to dash all their

hopes of regaining the throne of Hastinapur to the ground. Not only this, their supporter, King of Panchal, will have to accept our hegemony too."

"Karna ! your wisdom is really matchless and as for your strategic sense, it is unique too. But we must consult uncle Bhishma, Dronacharya and Vidur also. Having known their views, we shall be in a better position to plan our action," argued Dhritrashtra.

Dhritrashtra asked Duryodhana to direct the Prime Minister for arranging a meeting of the high-ups.

The meeting was arranged and discussions were started. Dhritrashtra laid Karna's plan before the Cabinet and asked Bhishma to express his opinion about it. Bhishma at once turned it down saying, "The Pandavas are as dear to me as you are. Yudhishthir has come of age and it is high time to give his father's throne back to him. The plan of invading Panchal is certainly an evil one. Duryodhana has already tried to liquidate the Pandavas in the lac-palace with the help of Purochan who fell a victim to his own misdeed. It should be an eye-opener for Duryodhana. He should come to the right path ; otherwise, he too is sure to meet with a similar fate."

Hearing Bhishma's words, Dhritrashtra hung his head down out of shame. But then, he requested Bhishma to do something for Duryodhana's interests also as

he was his eldest son and had always been dreaming of succeeding to the throne of Hastinapur.

Dronacharya also supported the view-point of Bhishma and asked Dhritrashtra to be just to his nephews. Discussions went on with Vidur participating actively in them.

At last it was decided that half the kingdom should be given to the Pandavas to avert the family crisis. Duryodhana and Dhritrashtra were made fully alive to the fact that the Pandavas were invincible.

Dhritrashtra had realised that the plans chalked out by Duryodhana and Karna could not be carried out in the face of opposition from the elders like Bhishma and Drona.

He had also followed that it was impossible to defeat the Pandavas who had Krishna and Balrama at their back and the powerful kingdom of Panchal bound to them through a matrimonial alliance.

Not only this, he had become aware that the approach of Duryodhana, Karna and Shakuni was sure to prove destructive for Hastinapur itself.

So, he decided to clean his hands from the stains of the misdeed of his son and to follow the advice of Bhishma.

So, Dhritrashtra said to Vidur, "Vidur ! I am not going to be misled by Duryodhana and Shakuni any more. My brother's sons are just my sons too. They deserve half the kingdom by all means. So, you should proceed to Panchal at once and bring my nephews, my daughter-in-law (Draupadi) and my sister-in-law (Kunti) with full State Honours."

Vidur, the Prime Minister of Hastinapur, taking valuable presents for the Pandavas along with a group of attendants, proceeded to Panchal with a view to bringing the Pandavas back to Hastinapur.

When Vidur got to the court of king Drupad, he was given a warm welcome. Formalities having been over, Vidur laid all the presents that he had brought from Hastinapur before the Pandavas.

The Prime Minister said, "Dhritrashtra, Bhishma, Drona and all the ladies of Hastinapur palace are very glad to know of the matrimonial alliance. Feeling sorry for what Duryodhana had done, they now crave the return of the Pandavas to Hastinapur. Gandhari is so curious to see Draupadi as soon as possible. So, I beg you to allow the Pandavas to leave for Hastinapur."

Luckily for the Pandavas, Krishna and Balrama had also reached Panchal a short time before the arrival of Vidur. So, King Drupad said to him, "It is not

for me to ask my sons-in-law to leave for Hastinapur, especially when I doubt their safety there. Who is ready to take the responsibility that Duryodhana would not harm them in any way there ? Even then, I leave it to Krishna, the best known well-wisher of my sons-in-law, to decide what to do."

So, Vidur turned to Krishna and Balrama to ask for their opinion.

Krishna opined that it was advisable to go and possess half the kingdom of Pandu and rule in peace building their Capital at a different place and hoped that this step would end the bad blood between the Kauravas and the Pandavas as well.

Seeking due permission of king Drupad, the Pandavas proceeded to Hastinapur along with Kunti and Draupadi escorted by Vidur and Krishna.

When they reached near Hastinapur, Drona, Kripacharya, Vikarna and other dignitaries came to receive them. A grand welcome was accorded to the princes whom people believed to have died in the lac-palace.

The residents of Hastinapur were no less delighted to see the Pandavas, Queen-mother (Kunti) and Draupadi.

They raised slogans in their glory and made merry in various ways. Yudhishthir, the eldest Pandava, was the main focus of people's attention.

They saw in him an image of their old King (Pandu) famous for his bravery and justice. They had full faith that Yudhishthir, when enthroned, would revive the old glory of Hastinapur.

The Pandavas touched the feet of Bhishma, Dronacharya, Dhritrashtra and other elders out of profound respect and they, in return, showered their heartiest benedictions upon them.

Gandhari was highly impatient to see Kunti, her sons and Draupadi. When they all entered the palace, her joy knew no bounds. She hugged each of them out of sincere affection, feeling sorry for what her son, Duryodhana, had done.

Next day, a meeting of Hastinapur Cabinet was held and the Pandavas went to the court on the invitation of Bhishma. They had been called to be informed that half the kingdom of Hastinapur was being given to them to end all the differences that had cropped up between them and the Kaurava Princes due to some misunderstandings.

Dhritrashtra said to Yudhishthir, "My son ! you are very wise and tolerant as well. There is no denying the fact that the throne of Hastinapur belongs solely to you. But my make-shift possession of it due to my brother's untimely death has incited Duryodhana to develop a longing to be the next ruler of Hastinapur. The family elders have decided to divide the kingdom into two

parts and hand over one part to you and the other to Duryodhana. I am sure that you will not disappoint me accepting this arrangement in the interest of the Kuru dynasty. It is sure to end all differences between you and Duryodhana as well. So, I would like you to proceed to *Khandavprastha* and make it the Capital of your part of the kingdom."

Yudhishthir, modest and accommodating as he was, gave his assent to the satisfaction of everybody, present in the court.

Bhishma and Dronacharya praised Yudhishthir for his accommodating nature and showered blessings on him.

So, Yudhishthir proceeded to Khandavprastha along with his brothers, mother and Draupadi. People of Khandavprastha received them with open arms.

In due course, Khandavprastha took the shape of a beautiful township which was named *Indraprastha.*

The Pandavas got a beautiful palace built in their new Capital. Within a short span of time, Indraprastha was glittering with glamour and soon excelled the grandeur of Hastinapur.

One day, when Yudhishthir was holding his court, Saint Narad happened to come there. He had come with the definite purpose of advising the five brothers regarding their common bride Draupadi. He told them the story of

two demon brothers—*Sund and Upsund*—who loved each other most dearly. But they quarrelled over a fairy-like damsel, *Tilottama*, and fought ferociously to be killed by each other.

So, the Pandavas drew up a code of conduct whereby each brother was to enjoy Draupadi's company for a month in his turn. Anybody violating the arrangement was to go into exile for 12 years.